HOKUSAI
The British Museum

ADDRESS BOOK

Pomegranate

SAN FRANCISCO

Published by Pomegranate Communications, Inc.
Box 808022, Petaluma, California 94975
800-227-1428; www.pomegranate.com

Pomegranate Europe Ltd.
Unit 1, Heathcote Business Centre, Hurlbutt Road
Warwick, Warwickshire CV34 6TD, U.K.
(44) 01926 430111

Cover image:
Katsushika Hokusai (1760–1849),
[Reflection in the] Surface of the Water, Misaka, Kai Province
From the series *Thirty-Six Views of Mt. Fuji*, 1830–1833
Color woodblock print, 25.3 x 37.5 cm (9^{15}/$_{16}$ x 14^{3}/$_{4}$ in.)
Published by Nishimuraya Yohachi

Pomegranate Catalog No. AA212
ISBN 0-7649-2574-1

Designed by Ronni Madrid

Printed in Korea

12 11 10 09 08 07 06 05 04 03   10 9 8 7 6 5 4 3 2 1

From about 1820 to about 1860, landscapes were especially popular subjects for Japanese printmakers. Beyond the sometimes quirky elegance of their composition, the prints functioned almost like the contents of a book; that is, they resembled postcards, or keepsakes, of the places they depicted. Perhaps that is why the great Japanese landscape prints are so powerfully evocative of things that they do not show: temperature and moisture; the sharpness or mildness of the air on one's face; the smell of flowers, grass, or snow. They engage one's senses and welcome the viewer into the places they depict.

The Japanese landscape style had grown away from Chinese-influenced idealization; Katsushika Hokusai (1760–1849) broke with the Japanese tradition in allowing European art to influence his woodblock prints. Especially in their perspectives, Hokusai's prints display a clear East/West fusion of styles. Two other distinctive qualities, the more so considering the multiblock print's demand of precision, are the freedom and the grace of his lines and shapes. The prints' lightness and lightheartedness distract the viewer from the extraordinary technical ability reflected in their execution.

Along with prints by other artists, Hokusai's prints found their way to Europe in mid-century. Enthusiastically received, they restored the balance of influence, changing the way Monet, Degas, and many other Impressionists saw the world.

Despite his wide renown and prodigious output, Hokusai was beset by misfortunes and lived his life in poverty. When he died, he left behind more than 30,000 print designs.

NAME	PHONE (H)
ADDRESS	PHONE (W)
	FAX
EMAIL	CELL/PAGER

NAME	PHONE (H)
ADDRESS	PHONE (W)
	FAX
EMAIL	CELL/PAGER

NAME	PHONE (H)
ADDRESS	PHONE (W)
	FAX
EMAIL	CELL/PAGER

NAME	PHONE (H)
ADDRESS	PHONE (W)
	FAX
EMAIL	CELL/PAGER

NAME	PHONE (H)
ADDRESS	PHONE (W)
	FAX
EMAIL	CELL/PAGER

NAME	PHONE (H)
ADDRESS	PHONE (W)
	FAX
EMAIL	CELL/PAGER

NAME	PHONE (H)
ADDRESS	PHONE (W)
	FAX
EMAIL	CELL/PAGER

NAME	PHONE (H)
ADDRESS	PHONE (W)
	FAX
EMAIL	CELL/PAGER

NAME	PHONE (H)
ADDRESS	PHONE (W)
	FAX
EMAIL	CELL/PAGER

NAME	PHONE (H)
ADDRESS	PHONE (W)
	FAX
EMAIL	CELL/PAGER

NAME	PHONE (H)
ADDRESS	PHONE (W)
	FAX
EMAIL	CELL/PAGER

NAME	PHONE (H)
ADDRESS	PHONE (W)
	FAX
EMAIL	CELL/PAGER

NAME

ADDRESS

EMAIL

PHONE (H)

PHONE (W)

FAX

CELL/PAGER

NAME

ADDRESS

EMAIL

PHONE (H)

PHONE (W)

FAX

CELL/PAGER

NAME

ADDRESS

EMAIL

PHONE (H)

PHONE (W)

FAX

CELL/PAGER

NAME

ADDRESS

EMAIL

PHONE (H)

PHONE (W)

FAX

CELL/PAGER

NAME

ADDRESS

EMAIL

PHONE (H)

PHONE (W)

FAX

CELL/PAGER

NAME

ADDRESS

EMAIL

PHONE (H)

PHONE (W)

FAX

CELL/PAGER

NAME	PHONE (H)
ADDRESS	PHONE (W)
	FAX
EMAIL	CELL/PAGER

NAME	PHONE (H)
ADDRESS	PHONE (W)
	FAX
EMAIL	CELL/PAGER

NAME	PHONE (H)
ADDRESS	PHONE (W)
	FAX
EMAIL	CELL/PAGER

NAME	PHONE (H)
ADDRESS	PHONE (W)
	FAX
EMAIL	CELL/PAGER

NAME	PHONE (H)
ADDRESS	PHONE (W)
	FAX
EMAIL	CELL/PAGER

NAME	PHONE (H)
ADDRESS	PHONE (W)
	FAX
EMAIL	CELL/PAGER

Yamabe no Akahito

From the series *One Hundred Poems by One Hundred Poets, Explained by the Nurse,* c. 1835–1836

Color woodblock print, 24.7 x 36.6 cm (9³⁄₄ x 14⁷⁄₁₆ in.)

Published by Nishimuraya Yohachi

Shichiri-ga-hama [Beach] in Suruga Province

From the series *Thirty-Six Views of Mt. Fuji*, 1830–1833

Color woodblock print, 24.4 x 36.4 cm (9⅝ x 14⁵⁄₁₆ in.)

Published by Nishimuraya Yohachi

NAME	PHONE (H)
ADDRESS	PHONE (W)
	FAX
EMAIL	CELL/PAGER

NAME	PHONE (H)
ADDRESS	PHONE (W)
	FAX
EMAIL	CELL/PAGER

NAME	PHONE (H)
ADDRESS	PHONE (W)
	FAX
EMAIL	CELL/PAGER

NAME	PHONE (H)
ADDRESS	PHONE (W)
	FAX
EMAIL	CELL/PAGER

NAME	PHONE (H)
ADDRESS	PHONE (W)
	FAX
EMAIL	CELL/PAGER

NAME	PHONE (H)
ADDRESS	PHONE (W)
	FAX
EMAIL	CELL/PAGER

NAME

ADDRESS

EMAIL

PHONE (H)

PHONE (W)

FAX

CELL/PAGER

NAME

ADDRESS

EMAIL

PHONE (H)

PHONE (W)

FAX

CELL/PAGER

NAME

ADDRESS

EMAIL

PHONE (H)

PHONE (W)

FAX

CELL/PAGER

NAME

ADDRESS

EMAIL

PHONE (H)

PHONE (W)

FAX

CELL/PAGER

NAME

ADDRESS

EMAIL

PHONE (H)

PHONE (W)

FAX

CELL/PAGER

NAME

ADDRESS

EMAIL

PHONE (H)

PHONE (W)

FAX

CELL/PAGER

NAME

ADDRESS

EMAIL

PHONE (H)

PHONE (W)

FAX

CELL/PAGER

NAME

ADDRESS

EMAIL

PHONE (H)

PHONE (W)

FAX

CELL/PAGER

NAME

ADDRESS

EMAIL

PHONE (H)

PHONE (W)

FAX

CELL/PAGER

NAME

ADDRESS

EMAIL

PHONE (H)

PHONE (W)

FAX

CELL/PAGER

NAME

ADDRESS

EMAIL

PHONE (H)

PHONE (W)

FAX

CELL/PAGER

NAME

ADDRESS

EMAIL

PHONE (H)

PHONE (W)

FAX

CELL/PAGER

NAME

ADDRESS

EMAIL

PHONE (H)

PHONE (W)

FAX

CELL/PAGER

NAME

ADDRESS

EMAIL

PHONE (H)

PHONE (W)

FAX

CELL/PAGER

NAME

ADDRESS

EMAIL

PHONE (H)

PHONE (W)

FAX

CELL/PAGER

NAME

ADDRESS

EMAIL

PHONE (H)

PHONE (W)

FAX

CELL/PAGER

NAME

ADDRESS

EMAIL

PHONE (H)

PHONE (W)

FAX

CELL/PAGER

NAME

ADDRESS

EMAIL

PHONE (H)

PHONE (W)

FAX

CELL/PAGER

Peasants by a Stream (detail)

From the *kyoka* album *The Mist of Sandara*

Woodblock, album plate, 21.4 x 31.8 cm (8⁷/₁₆ x 12¹/₂ in.)

Privately published by the Kasumi poetry club, 1797

Peasants by a Stream (detail)

From the *kyoka* album *The Mist of Sandara*

Woodblock, album plate, 21.4 x 31.8 cm (8⁷/₁₆ x 12½ in.)

Privately published by the Kasumi poetry club, 1797

NAME

ADDRESS

EMAIL

PHONE (H)

PHONE (W)

FAX

CELL/PAGER

NAME

ADDRESS

EMAIL

PHONE (H)

PHONE (W)

FAX

CELL/PAGER

NAME

ADDRESS

EMAIL

PHONE (H)

PHONE (W)

FAX

CELL/PAGER

NAME

ADDRESS

EMAIL

PHONE (H)

PHONE (W)

FAX

CELL/PAGER

NAME

ADDRESS

EMAIL

PHONE (H)

PHONE (W)

FAX

CELL/PAGER

NAME

ADDRESS

EMAIL

PHONE (H)

PHONE (W)

FAX

CELL/PAGER

NAME	PHONE (H)
ADDRESS	PHONE (W)
	FAX
EMAIL	CELL/PAGER

NAME	PHONE (H)
ADDRESS	PHONE (W)
	FAX
EMAIL	CELL/PAGER

NAME	PHONE (H)
ADDRESS	PHONE (W)
	FAX
EMAIL	CELL/PAGER

NAME	PHONE (H)
ADDRESS	PHONE (W)
	FAX
EMAIL	CELL/PAGER

NAME	PHONE (H)
ADDRESS	PHONE (W)
	FAX
EMAIL	CELL/PAGER

NAME	PHONE (H)
ADDRESS	PHONE (W)
	FAX
EMAIL	CELL/PAGER

NAME	PHONE (H)
ADDRESS	PHONE (W)
	FAX
EMAIL	CELL/PAGER

NAME	PHONE (H)
ADDRESS	PHONE (W)
	FAX
EMAIL	CELL/PAGER

NAME	PHONE (H)
ADDRESS	PHONE (W)
	FAX
EMAIL	CELL/PAGER

NAME	PHONE (H)
ADDRESS	PHONE (W)
	FAX
EMAIL	CELL/PAGER

NAME	PHONE (H)
ADDRESS	PHONE (W)
	FAX
EMAIL	CELL/PAGER

NAME	PHONE (H)
ADDRESS	PHONE (W)
	FAX
EMAIL	CELL/PAGER

NAME	PHONE (H)
ADDRESS	PHONE (W)
	FAX
EMAIL	CELL/PAGER

NAME	PHONE (H)
ADDRESS	PHONE (W)
	FAX
EMAIL	CELL/PAGER

NAME	PHONE (H)
ADDRESS	PHONE (W)
	FAX
EMAIL	CELL/PAGER

NAME	PHONE (H)
ADDRESS	PHONE (W)
	FAX
EMAIL	CELL/PAGER

NAME	PHONE (H)
ADDRESS	PHONE (W)
	FAX
EMAIL	CELL/PAGER

NAME	PHONE (H)
ADDRESS	PHONE (W)
	FAX
EMAIL	CELL/PAGER

Ushibori in Hitachi Province

From the series *Thirty-Six Views of Mt. Fuji,* 1830–1833
Color woodblock print, 24.4 x 36.4 cm (9⅝ x 14⁵⁄₁₆ in.)
Published by Nishimuraya Yohachi

Lake Suwa in Shinano Province

From the series *Thirty-Six Views of Mt. Fuji*, 1830–1833
Color woodblock print, 26.3 x 38.8 cm (10³/₈ x 15¹/₄ in.)
Published by Nishimuraya Yohachi

NAME

ADDRESS

EMAIL

PHONE (H)

PHONE (W)

FAX

CELL/PAGER

NAME

ADDRESS

EMAIL

PHONE (H)

PHONE (W)

FAX

CELL/PAGER

NAME

ADDRESS

EMAIL

PHONE (H)

PHONE (W)

FAX

CELL/PAGER

NAME

ADDRESS

EMAIL

PHONE (H)

PHONE (W)

FAX

CELL/PAGER

NAME

ADDRESS

EMAIL

PHONE (H)

PHONE (W)

FAX

CELL/PAGER

NAME

ADDRESS

EMAIL

PHONE (H)

PHONE (W)

FAX

CELL/PAGER

NAME

ADDRESS

EMAIL

PHONE (H)

PHONE (W)

FAX

CELL/PAGER

NAME

ADDRESS

EMAIL

PHONE (H)

PHONE (W)

FAX

CELL/PAGER

NAME

ADDRESS

EMAIL

PHONE (H)

PHONE (W)

FAX

CELL/PAGER

NAME

ADDRESS

EMAIL

PHONE (H)

PHONE (W)

FAX

CELL/PAGER

NAME

ADDRESS

EMAIL

PHONE (H)

PHONE (W)

FAX

CELL/PAGER

NAME

ADDRESS

EMAIL

PHONE (H)

PHONE (W)

FAX

CELL/PAGER

NAME

ADDRESS

EMAIL

PHONE (H)

PHONE (W)

FAX

CELL/PAGER

NAME

ADDRESS

EMAIL

PHONE (H)

PHONE (W)

FAX

CELL/PAGER

NAME

ADDRESS

EMAIL

PHONE (H)

PHONE (W)

FAX

CELL/PAGER

NAME

ADDRESS

EMAIL

PHONE (H)

PHONE (W)

FAX

CELL/PAGER

NAME

ADDRESS

EMAIL

PHONE (H)

PHONE (W)

FAX

CELL/PAGER

NAME

ADDRESS

EMAIL

PHONE (H)

PHONE (W)

FAX

CELL/PAGER

NAME	PHONE (H)
ADDRESS	PHONE (W)
	FAX
EMAIL	CELL/PAGER

NAME	PHONE (H)
ADDRESS	PHONE (W)
	FAX
EMAIL	CELL/PAGER

NAME	PHONE (H)
ADDRESS	PHONE (W)
	FAX
EMAIL	CELL/PAGER

NAME	PHONE (H)
ADDRESS	PHONE (W)
	FAX
EMAIL	CELL/PAGER

NAME	PHONE (H)
ADDRESS	PHONE (W)
	FAX
EMAIL	CELL/PAGER

NAME	PHONE (H)
ADDRESS	PHONE (W)
	FAX
EMAIL	CELL/PAGER

Kajikazawa in Kai Province

From the series *Thirty-Six Views of Mt. Fuji*, 1830–1833
Color woodblock print, 26.1 x 38.3 cm (10¼ x 15¹/₁₆ in.)
Published by Nishimuraya Yohachi

Bellflower and Dragonfly
Color woodblock print, 26 x 37.5 cm (10¼ x 14¾ in.)

NAME	PHONE (H)
ADDRESS	PHONE (W)
	FAX
EMAIL	CELL/PAGER

NAME	PHONE (H)
ADDRESS	PHONE (W)
	FAX
EMAIL	CELL/PAGER

NAME	PHONE (H)
ADDRESS	PHONE (W)
	FAX
EMAIL	CELL/PAGER

NAME	PHONE (H)
ADDRESS	PHONE (W)
	FAX
EMAIL	CELL/PAGER

NAME	PHONE (H)
ADDRESS	PHONE (W)
	FAX
EMAIL	CELL/PAGER

NAME	PHONE (H)
ADDRESS	PHONE (W)
	FAX
EMAIL	CELL/PAGER

NAME

ADDRESS

EMAIL

PHONE (H)

PHONE (W)

FAX

CELL/PAGER

NAME

ADDRESS

EMAIL

PHONE (H)

PHONE (W)

FAX

CELL/PAGER

NAME

ADDRESS

EMAIL

PHONE (H)

PHONE (W)

FAX

CELL/PAGER

NAME

ADDRESS

EMAIL

PHONE (H)

PHONE (W)

FAX

CELL/PAGER

NAME

ADDRESS

EMAIL

PHONE (H)

PHONE (W)

FAX

CELL/PAGER

NAME

ADDRESS

EMAIL

PHONE (H)

PHONE (W)

FAX

CELL/PAGER

NAME

ADDRESS

EMAIL

PHONE (H)

PHONE (W)

FAX

CELL/PAGER

NAME

ADDRESS

EMAIL

PHONE (H)

PHONE (W)

FAX

CELL/PAGER

NAME

ADDRESS

EMAIL

PHONE (H)

PHONE (W)

FAX

CELL/PAGER

NAME

ADDRESS

EMAIL

PHONE (H)

PHONE (W)

FAX

CELL/PAGER

NAME

ADDRESS

EMAIL

PHONE (H)

PHONE (W)

FAX

CELL/PAGER

NAME

ADDRESS

EMAIL

PHONE (H)

PHONE (W)

FAX

CELL/PAGER

NAME	PHONE (H)
ADDRESS	PHONE (W)
	FAX
EMAIL	CELL/PAGER

NAME	PHONE (H)
ADDRESS	PHONE (W)
	FAX
EMAIL	CELL/PAGER

NAME	PHONE (H)
ADDRESS	PHONE (W)
	FAX
EMAIL	CELL/PAGER

NAME	PHONE (H)
ADDRESS	PHONE (W)
	FAX
EMAIL	CELL/PAGER

NAME	PHONE (H)
ADDRESS	PHONE (W)
	FAX
EMAIL	CELL/PAGER

NAME	PHONE (H)
ADDRESS	PHONE (W)
	FAX
EMAIL	CELL/PAGER

Umezawa Manor in Sagami Province

From the series *Thirty-Six Views of Mt. Fuji*, 1830–1833
Color woodblock print, 25.6 x 38.1 cm (10¹/₁₆ x 15 in.)
Published by Nishimuraya Yohachi

Ejiri in Suruga Province

From the series *Thirty-Six Views of Mt. Fuji*, 1830–1833

Color woodblock print, 25.9 x 38.2 cm (10³/₁₆ x 15¹/₁₆ in.)

Published by Nishimuraya Yohachi

NAME	PHONE (H)
ADDRESS	PHONE (W)
	FAX
EMAIL	CELL/PAGER

NAME	PHONE (H)
ADDRESS	PHONE (W)
	FAX
EMAIL	CELL/PAGER

NAME	PHONE (H)
ADDRESS	PHONE (W)
	FAX
EMAIL	CELL/PAGER

NAME	PHONE (H)
ADDRESS	PHONE (W)
	FAX
EMAIL	CELL/PAGER

NAME	PHONE (H)
ADDRESS	PHONE (W)
	FAX
EMAIL	CELL/PAGER

NAME	PHONE (H)
ADDRESS	PHONE (W)
	FAX
EMAIL	CELL/PAGER

NAME

ADDRESS

EMAIL

PHONE (H)

PHONE (W)

FAX

CELL/PAGER

NAME

ADDRESS

EMAIL

PHONE (H)

PHONE (W)

FAX

CELL/PAGER

NAME

ADDRESS

EMAIL

PHONE (H)

PHONE (W)

FAX

CELL/PAGER

NAME

ADDRESS

EMAIL

PHONE (H)

PHONE (W)

FAX

CELL/PAGER

NAME

ADDRESS

EMAIL

PHONE (H)

PHONE (W)

FAX

CELL/PAGER

NAME

ADDRESS

EMAIL

PHONE (H)

PHONE (W)

FAX

CELL/PAGER

NAME		PHONE (H)	
ADDRESS		PHONE (W)	
		FAX	
EMAIL		CELL/PAGER	

NAME		PHONE (H)	
ADDRESS		PHONE (W)	
		FAX	
EMAIL		CELL/PAGER	

NAME		PHONE (H)	
ADDRESS		PHONE (W)	
		FAX	
EMAIL		CELL/PAGER	

NAME		PHONE (H)	
ADDRESS		PHONE (W)	
		FAX	
EMAIL		CELL/PAGER	

NAME		PHONE (H)	
ADDRESS		PHONE (W)	
		FAX	
EMAIL		CELL/PAGER	

NAME		PHONE (H)	
ADDRESS		PHONE (W)	
		FAX	
EMAIL		CELL/PAGER	

NAME	PHONE (H)
ADDRESS	PHONE (W)
	FAX
EMAIL	CELL/PAGER

NAME	PHONE (H)
ADDRESS	PHONE (W)
	FAX
EMAIL	CELL/PAGER

NAME	PHONE (H)
ADDRESS	PHONE (W)
	FAX
EMAIL	CELL/PAGER

NAME	PHONE (H)
ADDRESS	PHONE (W)
	FAX
EMAIL	CELL/PAGER

NAME	PHONE (H)
ADDRESS	PHONE (W)
	FAX
EMAIL	CELL/PAGER

NAME	PHONE (H)
ADDRESS	PHONE (W)
	FAX
EMAIL	CELL/PAGER

Mishima Pass in Kai Province

From the series *Thirty-Six Views of Mt. Fuji*, 1830–1833
Color woodblock print, 25.4 x 37.3 cm (10 x 14¹¹/₁₆ in.)
Published by Nishimuraya Yohachi

Three Men Picnicking by Amida Waterfall
[Amida Waterfall on the Kisokaido Road]

Color woodblock print, 37.5 x 24.8 cm (14¾ x 9¾ in.)

NAME _____ PHONE (H) _____

ADDRESS _____ PHONE (W) _____

_____ FAX _____

EMAIL _____ CELL/PAGER _____

NAME _____ PHONE (H) _____

ADDRESS _____ PHONE (W) _____

_____ FAX _____

EMAIL _____ CELL/PAGER _____

NAME _____ PHONE (H) _____

ADDRESS _____ PHONE (W) _____

_____ FAX _____

EMAIL _____ CELL/PAGER _____

NAME _____ PHONE (H) _____

ADDRESS _____ PHONE (W) _____

_____ FAX _____

EMAIL _____ CELL/PAGER _____

NAME _____ PHONE (H) _____

ADDRESS _____ PHONE (W) _____

_____ FAX _____

EMAIL _____ CELL/PAGER _____

NAME _____ PHONE (H) _____

ADDRESS _____ PHONE (W) _____

_____ FAX _____

EMAIL _____ CELL/PAGER _____

NAME	PHONE (H)
ADDRESS	PHONE (W)
	FAX
EMAIL	CELL/PAGER

NAME	PHONE (H)
ADDRESS	PHONE (W)
	FAX
EMAIL	CELL/PAGER

NAME	PHONE (H)
ADDRESS	PHONE (W)
	FAX
EMAIL	CELL/PAGER

NAME	PHONE (H)
ADDRESS	PHONE (W)
	FAX
EMAIL	CELL/PAGER

NAME	PHONE (H)
ADDRESS	PHONE (W)
	FAX
EMAIL	CELL/PAGER

NAME	PHONE (H)
ADDRESS	PHONE (W)
	FAX
EMAIL	CELL/PAGER

NAME

ADDRESS

EMAIL

PHONE (H)

PHONE (W)

FAX

CELL/PAGER

NAME

ADDRESS

EMAIL

PHONE (H)

PHONE (W)

FAX

CELL/PAGER

NAME

ADDRESS

EMAIL

PHONE (H)

PHONE (W)

FAX

CELL/PAGER

NAME

ADDRESS

EMAIL

PHONE (H)

PHONE (W)

FAX

CELL/PAGER

NAME

ADDRESS

EMAIL

PHONE (H)

PHONE (W)

FAX

CELL/PAGER

NAME

ADDRESS

EMAIL

PHONE (H)

PHONE (W)

FAX

CELL/PAGER

NAME	PHONE (H)
ADDRESS	PHONE (W)
	FAX
EMAIL	CELL/PAGER

NAME	PHONE (H)
ADDRESS	PHONE (W)
	FAX
EMAIL	CELL/PAGER

NAME	PHONE (H)
ADDRESS	PHONE (W)
	FAX
EMAIL	CELL/PAGER

NAME	PHONE (H)
ADDRESS	PHONE (W)
	FAX
EMAIL	CELL/PAGER

NAME	PHONE (H)
ADDRESS	PHONE (W)
	FAX
EMAIL	CELL/PAGER

NAME	PHONE (H)
ADDRESS	PHONE (W)
	FAX
EMAIL	CELL/PAGER

Under the Wave, off Kanagawa [The Great Wave]

From the series *Thirty-Six Views of Mt. Fuji*, 1830–1833

Color woodblock print, 25.9 x 37.2 cm (10³/₁₆ x 14⅝ in.)

Published by Nishimuraya Yohachi

Parody of Narihira's Journey to the East, c. 1805–1810

Color woodblock print, large *surimono* (folded), 42.5 x 57.5 cm (16¾ x 22⅝ in.)

NAME

ADDRESS

EMAIL

PHONE (H)

PHONE (W)

FAX

CELL/PAGER

NAME

ADDRESS

EMAIL

PHONE (H)

PHONE (W)

FAX

CELL/PAGER

NAME

ADDRESS

EMAIL

PHONE (H)

PHONE (W)

FAX

CELL/PAGER

NAME

ADDRESS

EMAIL

PHONE (H)

PHONE (W)

FAX

CELL/PAGER

NAME

ADDRESS

EMAIL

PHONE (H)

PHONE (W)

FAX

CELL/PAGER

NAME

ADDRESS

EMAIL

PHONE (H)

PHONE (W)

FAX

CELL/PAGER

NAME		PHONE (H)
ADDRESS		PHONE (W)
		FAX
EMAIL		CELL/PAGER

NAME		PHONE (H)
ADDRESS		PHONE (W)
		FAX
EMAIL		CELL/PAGER

NAME		PHONE (H)
ADDRESS		PHONE (W)
		FAX
EMAIL		CELL/PAGER

NAME		PHONE (H)
ADDRESS		PHONE (W)
		FAX
EMAIL		CELL/PAGER

NAME		PHONE (H)
ADDRESS		PHONE (W)
		FAX
EMAIL		CELL/PAGER

NAME		PHONE (H)
ADDRESS		PHONE (W)
		FAX
EMAIL		CELL/PAGER

NAME

ADDRESS

EMAIL

PHONE (H)

PHONE (W)

FAX

CELL/PAGER

NAME

ADDRESS

EMAIL

PHONE (H)

PHONE (W)

FAX

CELL/PAGER

NAME

ADDRESS

EMAIL

PHONE (H)

PHONE (W)

FAX

CELL/PAGER

NAME

ADDRESS

EMAIL

PHONE (H)

PHONE (W)

FAX

CELL/PAGER

NAME

ADDRESS

EMAIL

PHONE (H)

PHONE (W)

FAX

CELL/PAGER

NAME

ADDRESS

EMAIL

PHONE (H)

PHONE (W)

FAX

CELL/PAGER

NAME	PHONE (H)
ADDRESS	PHONE (W)
	FAX
EMAIL	CELL/PAGER

NAME	PHONE (H)
ADDRESS	PHONE (W)
	FAX
EMAIL	CELL/PAGER

NAME	PHONE (H)
ADDRESS	PHONE (W)
	FAX
EMAIL	CELL/PAGER

NAME	PHONE (H)
ADDRESS	PHONE (W)
	FAX
EMAIL	CELL/PAGER

NAME	PHONE (H)
ADDRESS	PHONE (W)
	FAX
EMAIL	CELL/PAGER

NAME	PHONE (H)
ADDRESS	PHONE (W)
	FAX
EMAIL	CELL/PAGER

Rainstorm Beneath the Summit

From the series *Thirty-Six Views of Mt. Fuji,* 1830–1833
Color woodblock print, 24.1 x 36.5 cm (9$\frac{1}{2}$ x 14$\frac{3}{8}$ in.)
Published by Nishimuraya Yohachi

A Young Man on a White Horse
[Youth Setting Out from Home] [Shonenko]

Woodblock, *nagaban,* 50 x 22.6 cm (19¹¹/₁₆ x 8⅞ in.)

NAME

ADDRESS

EMAIL

PHONE (H)

PHONE (W)

FAX

CELL/PAGER

NAME

ADDRESS

EMAIL

PHONE (H)

PHONE (W)

FAX

CELL/PAGER

NAME

ADDRESS

EMAIL

PHONE (H)

PHONE (W)

FAX

CELL/PAGER

NAME

ADDRESS

EMAIL

PHONE (H)

PHONE (W)

FAX

CELL/PAGER

NAME

ADDRESS

EMAIL

PHONE (H)

PHONE (W)

FAX

CELL/PAGER

NAME

ADDRESS

EMAIL

PHONE (H)

PHONE (W)

FAX

CELL/PAGER

NAME

ADDRESS

EMAIL

PHONE (H)

PHONE (W)

FAX

CELL/PAGER

NAME

ADDRESS

EMAIL

PHONE (H)

PHONE (W)

FAX

CELL/PAGER

NAME

ADDRESS

EMAIL

PHONE (H)

PHONE (W)

FAX

CELL/PAGER

NAME

ADDRESS

EMAIL

PHONE (H)

PHONE (W)

FAX

CELL/PAGER

NAME

ADDRESS

EMAIL

PHONE (H)

PHONE (W)

FAX

CELL/PAGER

NAME

ADDRESS

EMAIL

PHONE (H)

PHONE (W)

FAX

CELL/PAGER

NAME

ADDRESS

EMAIL

PHONE (H)

PHONE (W)

FAX

CELL/PAGER

NAME

ADDRESS

EMAIL

PHONE (H)

PHONE (W)

FAX

CELL/PAGER

NAME

ADDRESS

EMAIL

PHONE (H)

PHONE (W)

FAX

CELL/PAGER

NAME

ADDRESS

EMAIL

PHONE (H)

PHONE (W)

FAX

CELL/PAGER

NAME

ADDRESS

EMAIL

PHONE (H)

PHONE (W)

FAX

CELL/PAGER

NAME

ADDRESS

EMAIL

PHONE (H)

PHONE (W)

FAX

CELL/PAGER

NAME	PHONE (H)
ADDRESS	PHONE (W)
	FAX
EMAIL	CELL/PAGER

NAME	PHONE (H)
ADDRESS	PHONE (W)
	FAX
EMAIL	CELL/PAGER

NAME	PHONE (H)
ADDRESS	PHONE (W)
	FAX
EMAIL	CELL/PAGER

NAME	PHONE (H)
ADDRESS	PHONE (W)
	FAX
EMAIL	CELL/PAGER

NAME	PHONE (H)
ADDRESS	PHONE (W)
	FAX
EMAIL	CELL/PAGER

NAME	PHONE (H)
ADDRESS	PHONE (W)
	FAX
EMAIL	CELL/PAGER

Suruga Street in Edo, the Mitsui Store, Simplified View

From the series *Thirty-Six Views of Mt. Fuji*, 1830–1833

Color woodblock print, 24.6 x 36.6 cm ($9^{11}/_{16}$ x $14^7/_{16}$ in.)

Published by Nishimuraya Yohachi

Viewing Sunset over Ryōgoku Bridge from
the Ommaya Embankment [Edo]
From the series *Thirty-Six Views of Mt. Fuji*, 1830–1833
Color woodblock print, 24.6 x 37.8 cm (9¹¹/₁₆ x 14⁷/₈ in.)
Published by Nishimuraya Yohachi

NAME

ADDRESS

EMAIL

PHONE (H)

PHONE (W)

FAX

CELL/PAGER

NAME

ADDRESS

EMAIL

PHONE (H)

PHONE (W)

FAX

CELL/PAGER

NAME

ADDRESS

EMAIL

PHONE (H)

PHONE (W)

FAX

CELL/PAGER

NAME

ADDRESS

EMAIL

PHONE (H)

PHONE (W)

FAX

CELL/PAGER

NAME

ADDRESS

EMAIL

PHONE (H)

PHONE (W)

FAX

CELL/PAGER

NAME

ADDRESS

EMAIL

PHONE (H)

PHONE (W)

FAX

CELL/PAGER

NAME _____   PHONE (H) _____

ADDRESS _____   PHONE (W) _____

_____   FAX _____

EMAIL _____   CELL/PAGER _____

NAME _____   PHONE (H) _____

ADDRESS _____   PHONE (W) _____

_____   FAX _____

EMAIL _____   CELL/PAGER _____

NAME _____   PHONE (H) _____

ADDRESS _____   PHONE (W) _____

_____   FAX _____

EMAIL _____   CELL/PAGER _____

NAME _____   PHONE (H) _____

ADDRESS _____   PHONE (W) _____

_____   FAX _____

EMAIL _____   CELL/PAGER _____

NAME _____   PHONE (H) _____

ADDRESS _____   PHONE (W) _____

_____   FAX _____

EMAIL _____   CELL/PAGER _____

NAME _____   PHONE (H) _____

ADDRESS _____   PHONE (W) _____

_____   FAX _____

EMAIL _____   CELL/PAGER _____

NAME

ADDRESS

EMAIL

PHONE (H)

PHONE (W)

FAX

CELL/PAGER

NAME

ADDRESS

EMAIL

PHONE (H)

PHONE (W)

FAX

CELL/PAGER

NAME

ADDRESS

EMAIL

PHONE (H)

PHONE (W)

FAX

CELL/PAGER

NAME

ADDRESS

EMAIL

PHONE (H)

PHONE (W)

FAX

CELL/PAGER

NAME

ADDRESS

EMAIL

PHONE (H)

PHONE (W)

FAX

CELL/PAGER

NAME

ADDRESS

EMAIL

PHONE (H)

PHONE (W)

FAX

CELL/PAGER

NAME	PHONE (H)
ADDRESS	PHONE (W)
	FAX
EMAIL	CELL/PAGER

NAME	PHONE (H)
ADDRESS	PHONE (W)
	FAX
EMAIL	CELL/PAGER

NAME	PHONE (H)
ADDRESS	PHONE (W)
	FAX
EMAIL	CELL/PAGER

NAME	PHONE (H)
ADDRESS	PHONE (W)
	FAX
EMAIL	CELL/PAGER

NAME	PHONE (H)
ADDRESS	PHONE (W)
	FAX
EMAIL	CELL/PAGER

NAME	PHONE (H)
ADDRESS	PHONE (W)
	FAX
EMAIL	CELL/PAGER

Turban Shell Hall of the Five Hundred Arhat Temple [Edo]

From the series *Thirty-Six Views of Mt. Fuji*, 1830–1833

Color woodblock print, 24.7 x 37.3 cm (9³⁄₄ x 14¹¹⁄₁₆ in.)

Published by Nishimuraya Yohachi

Pleasure Boats on Sumida River

Color woodblock print, 26 x 37.3 cm (10¼ x 14¹¹⁄₁₆ in.)

NAME

ADDRESS

EMAIL

PHONE (H)

PHONE (W)

FAX

CELL/PAGER

NAME

ADDRESS

EMAIL

PHONE (H)

PHONE (W)

FAX

CELL/PAGER

NAME

ADDRESS

EMAIL

PHONE (H)

PHONE (W)

FAX

CELL/PAGER

NAME

ADDRESS

EMAIL

PHONE (H)

PHONE (W)

FAX

CELL/PAGER

NAME

ADDRESS

EMAIL

PHONE (H)

PHONE (W)

FAX

CELL/PAGER

NAME

ADDRESS

EMAIL

PHONE (H)

PHONE (W)

FAX

CELL/PAGER

NAME	PHONE (H)
ADDRESS	PHONE (W)
	FAX
EMAIL	CELL/PAGER

NAME	PHONE (H)
ADDRESS	PHONE (W)
	FAX
EMAIL	CELL/PAGER

NAME	PHONE (H)
ADDRESS	PHONE (W)
	FAX
EMAIL	CELL/PAGER

NAME	PHONE (H)
ADDRESS	PHONE (W)
	FAX
EMAIL	CELL/PAGER

NAME	PHONE (H)
ADDRESS	PHONE (W)
	FAX
EMAIL	CELL/PAGER

NAME	PHONE (H)
ADDRESS	PHONE (W)
	FAX
EMAIL	CELL/PAGER

NAME	PHONE (H)
ADDRESS	PHONE (W)
	FAX
EMAIL	CELL/PAGER

NAME	PHONE (H)
ADDRESS	PHONE (W)
	FAX
EMAIL	CELL/PAGER

NAME	PHONE (H)
ADDRESS	PHONE (W)
	FAX
EMAIL	CELL/PAGER

NAME	PHONE (H)
ADDRESS	PHONE (W)
	FAX
EMAIL	CELL/PAGER

NAME	PHONE (H)
ADDRESS	PHONE (W)
	FAX
EMAIL	CELL/PAGER

NAME	PHONE (H)
ADDRESS	PHONE (W)
	FAX
EMAIL	CELL/PAGER

NAME	PHONE (H)
ADDRESS	PHONE (W)
	FAX
EMAIL	CELL/PAGER

NAME	PHONE (H)
ADDRESS	PHONE (W)
	FAX
EMAIL	CELL/PAGER

NAME	PHONE (H)
ADDRESS	PHONE (W)
	FAX
EMAIL	CELL/PAGER

NAME	PHONE (H)
ADDRESS	PHONE (W)
	FAX
EMAIL	CELL/PAGER

NAME	PHONE (H)
ADDRESS	PHONE (W)
	FAX
EMAIL	CELL/PAGER

NAME	PHONE (H)
ADDRESS	PHONE (W)
	FAX
EMAIL	CELL/PAGER

Snowy Morning at Koishikawa

From the series *Thirty-Six Views of Mt. Fuji*, 1830–1833
Color woodblock print, 25.1 x 37.1 cm (9⁷/₈ x 14⁵/₈ in.)
Published by Nishimuraya Yohachi

Waterwheel at Onden

From the series *Thirty-Six Views of Mt. Fuji*, 1830–1833
Color woodblock print, 25.1 x 37.9 cm (9⁷/₈ x 14¹⁵/₁₆ in.)
Published by Nishimuraya Yohachi

NAME	PHONE (H)
ADDRESS	PHONE (W)
	FAX
EMAIL	CELL/PAGER

NAME	PHONE (H)
ADDRESS	PHONE (W)
	FAX
EMAIL	CELL/PAGER

NAME	PHONE (H)
ADDRESS	PHONE (W)
	FAX
EMAIL	CELL/PAGER

NAME	PHONE (H)
ADDRESS	PHONE (W)
	FAX
EMAIL	CELL/PAGER

NAME	PHONE (H)
ADDRESS	PHONE (W)
	FAX
EMAIL	CELL/PAGER

NAME	PHONE (H)
ADDRESS	PHONE (W)
	FAX
EMAIL	CELL/PAGER

NAME	PHONE (H)
ADDRESS	PHONE (W)
	FAX
EMAIL	CELL/PAGER

NAME	PHONE (H)
ADDRESS	PHONE (W)
	FAX
EMAIL	CELL/PAGER

NAME	PHONE (H)
ADDRESS	PHONE (W)
	FAX
EMAIL	CELL/PAGER

NAME	PHONE (H)
ADDRESS	PHONE (W)
	FAX
EMAIL	CELL/PAGER

NAME	PHONE (H)
ADDRESS	PHONE (W)
	FAX
EMAIL	CELL/PAGER

NAME	PHONE (H)
ADDRESS	PHONE (W)
	FAX
EMAIL	CELL/PAGER

NAME	PHONE (H)
ADDRESS	PHONE (W)
	FAX
EMAIL	CELL/PAGER

NAME	PHONE (H)
ADDRESS	PHONE (W)
	FAX
EMAIL	CELL/PAGER

NAME	PHONE (H)
ADDRESS	PHONE (W)
	FAX
EMAIL	CELL/PAGER

NAME	PHONE (H)
ADDRESS	PHONE (W)
	FAX
EMAIL	CELL/PAGER

NAME	PHONE (H)
ADDRESS	PHONE (W)
	FAX
EMAIL	CELL/PAGER

NAME	PHONE (H)
ADDRESS	PHONE (W)
	FAX
EMAIL	CELL/PAGER

NAME	PHONE (H)
ADDRESS	PHONE (W)
	FAX
EMAIL	CELL/PAGER

NAME	PHONE (H)
ADDRESS	PHONE (W)
	FAX
EMAIL	CELL/PAGER

NAME	PHONE (H)
ADDRESS	PHONE (W)
	FAX
EMAIL	CELL/PAGER

NAME	PHONE (H)
ADDRESS	PHONE (W)
	FAX
EMAIL	CELL/PAGER

NAME	PHONE (H)
ADDRESS	PHONE (W)
	FAX
EMAIL	CELL/PAGER

NAME	PHONE (H)
ADDRESS	PHONE (W)
	FAX
EMAIL	CELL/PAGER

Simplified View, Tago Beach, [near] Ejiri
on the Tōkaidō Highway

From the series *Thirty-Six Views of Mt. Fuji*, 1830–1833

Color woodblock print, 25.2 x 36 cm (9^{15}/$_{16}$ x 14^{3}/$_{16}$ in.)

Published by Nishimuraya Yohachi

Fishermen Hauling a Net

Color woodblock print, 26.1 x 37.5 cm (10¼ x 14¾ in.)

NAME

ADDRESS

EMAIL

PHONE (H)

PHONE (W)

FAX

CELL/PAGER

NAME

ADDRESS

EMAIL

PHONE (H)

PHONE (W)

FAX

CELL/PAGER

NAME

ADDRESS

EMAIL

PHONE (H)

PHONE (W)

FAX

CELL/PAGER

NAME

ADDRESS

EMAIL

PHONE (H)

PHONE (W)

FAX

CELL/PAGER

NAME

ADDRESS

EMAIL

PHONE (H)

PHONE (W)

FAX

CELL/PAGER

NAME

ADDRESS

EMAIL

PHONE (H)

PHONE (W)

FAX

CELL/PAGER

NAME	PHONE (H)
ADDRESS	PHONE (W)
	FAX
EMAIL	CELL/PAGER

NAME	PHONE (H)
ADDRESS	PHONE (W)
	FAX
EMAIL	CELL/PAGER

NAME	PHONE (H)
ADDRESS	PHONE (W)
	FAX
EMAIL	CELL/PAGER

NAME	PHONE (H)
ADDRESS	PHONE (W)
	FAX
EMAIL	CELL/PAGER

NAME	PHONE (H)
ADDRESS	PHONE (W)
	FAX
EMAIL	CELL/PAGER

NAME	PHONE (H)
ADDRESS	PHONE (W)
	FAX
EMAIL	CELL/PAGER

NAME

ADDRESS

EMAIL

PHONE (H)

PHONE (W)

FAX

CELL/PAGER

NAME

ADDRESS

EMAIL

PHONE (H)

PHONE (W)

FAX

CELL/PAGER

NAME

ADDRESS

EMAIL

PHONE (H)

PHONE (W)

FAX

CELL/PAGER

NAME

ADDRESS

EMAIL

PHONE (H)

PHONE (W)

FAX

CELL/PAGER

NAME

ADDRESS

EMAIL

PHONE (H)

PHONE (W)

FAX

CELL/PAGER

NAME

ADDRESS

EMAIL

PHONE (H)

PHONE (W)

FAX

CELL/PAGER

NAME

ADDRESS

EMAIL

PHONE (H)

PHONE (W)

FAX

CELL/PAGER

NAME

ADDRESS

EMAIL

PHONE (H)

PHONE (W)

FAX

CELL/PAGER

NAME

ADDRESS

EMAIL

PHONE (H)

PHONE (W)

FAX

CELL/PAGER

NAME

ADDRESS

EMAIL

PHONE (H)

PHONE (W)

FAX

CELL/PAGER

NAME

ADDRESS

EMAIL

PHONE (H)

PHONE (W)

FAX

CELL/PAGER

NAME

ADDRESS

EMAIL

PHONE (H)

PHONE (W)

FAX

CELL/PAGER

Sekiya Villages on the Sumida River [Edo]

From the series *Thirty-Six Views of Mt. Fuji*, 1830–1833

Color woodblock print, 25.6 x 37.6 cm (10¹/₁₆ x 14¹³/₁₆ in.)

Published by Nishimuraya Yohachi

[Reflection in the] Surface of the Water, Misaka, Kai Province

From the series *Thirty-Six Views of Mt. Fuji*, 1830–1833

Color woodblock print, 25.3 x 37.5 cm ($9^{15}/_{16}$ x $14^{3}/_{4}$ in.)

Published by Nishimuraya Yohachi

NAME

ADDRESS

EMAIL

PHONE (H)

PHONE (W)

FAX

CELL/PAGER

NAME

ADDRESS

EMAIL

PHONE (H)

PHONE (W)

FAX

CELL/PAGER

NAME

ADDRESS

EMAIL

PHONE (H)

PHONE (W)

FAX

CELL/PAGER

NAME

ADDRESS

EMAIL

PHONE (H)

PHONE (W)

FAX

CELL/PAGER

NAME

ADDRESS

EMAIL

PHONE (H)

PHONE (W)

FAX

CELL/PAGER

NAME

ADDRESS

EMAIL

PHONE (H)

PHONE (W)

FAX

CELL/PAGER

NAME

ADDRESS

EMAIL

PHONE (H)

PHONE (W)

FAX

CELL/PAGER

NAME

ADDRESS

EMAIL

PHONE (H)

PHONE (W)

FAX

CELL/PAGER

NAME

ADDRESS

EMAIL

PHONE (H)

PHONE (W)

FAX

CELL/PAGER

NAME

ADDRESS

EMAIL

PHONE (H)

PHONE (W)

FAX

CELL/PAGER

NAME

ADDRESS

EMAIL

PHONE (H)

PHONE (W)

FAX

CELL/PAGER

NAME

ADDRESS

EMAIL

PHONE (H)

PHONE (W)

FAX

CELL/PAGER

NAME	PHONE (H)
ADDRESS	PHONE (W)
	FAX
EMAIL	CELL/PAGER

NAME	PHONE (H)
ADDRESS	PHONE (W)
	FAX
EMAIL	CELL/PAGER

NAME	PHONE (H)
ADDRESS	PHONE (W)
	FAX
EMAIL	CELL/PAGER

NAME	PHONE (H)
ADDRESS	PHONE (W)
	FAX
EMAIL	CELL/PAGER

NAME	PHONE (H)
ADDRESS	PHONE (W)
	FAX
EMAIL	CELL/PAGER

NAME	PHONE (H)
ADDRESS	PHONE (W)
	FAX
EMAIL	CELL/PAGER

NAME	PHONE (H)
ADDRESS	PHONE (W)
	FAX
EMAIL	CELL/PAGER

NAME	PHONE (H)
ADDRESS	PHONE (W)
	FAX
EMAIL	CELL/PAGER

NAME	PHONE (H)
ADDRESS	PHONE (W)
	FAX
EMAIL	CELL/PAGER

NAME	PHONE (H)
ADDRESS	PHONE (W)
	FAX
EMAIL	CELL/PAGER

NAME	PHONE (H)
ADDRESS	PHONE (W)
	FAX
EMAIL	CELL/PAGER

NAME	PHONE (H)
ADDRESS	PHONE (W)
	FAX
EMAIL	CELL/PAGER

Hodogaya on the Tōkaidō Highway

From the series *Thirty-Six Views of Mt. Fuji*, 1830–1833

Color woodblock print, 25.3 x 38.2 cm (9¹⁵/₁₆ x 15¹/₁₆ in.)

Published by Nishimuraya Yohachi

A Branch of Plum

From the privately published *kyoka* album *The Nightingale of Miayama*, c. 1798
Woodblock, album plate, 19.4 x 26.3 cm (7⅝ x 10⅜ in.)

NAME	PHONE (H)
ADDRESS	PHONE (W)
	FAX
EMAIL	CELL/PAGER

NAME	PHONE (H)
ADDRESS	PHONE (W)
	FAX
EMAIL	CELL/PAGER

NAME	PHONE (H)
ADDRESS	PHONE (W)
	FAX
EMAIL	CELL/PAGER

NAME	PHONE (H)
ADDRESS	PHONE (W)
	FAX
EMAIL	CELL/PAGER

NAME	PHONE (H)
ADDRESS	PHONE (W)
	FAX
EMAIL	CELL/PAGER

NAME	PHONE (H)
ADDRESS	PHONE (W)
	FAX
EMAIL	CELL/PAGER

NAME

ADDRESS

EMAIL

PHONE (H)

PHONE (W)

FAX

CELL/PAGER

NAME

ADDRESS

EMAIL

PHONE (H)

PHONE (W)

FAX

CELL/PAGER

NAME

ADDRESS

EMAIL

PHONE (H)

PHONE (W)

FAX

CELL/PAGER

NAME

ADDRESS

EMAIL

PHONE (H)

PHONE (W)

FAX

CELL/PAGER

NAME

ADDRESS

EMAIL

PHONE (H)

PHONE (W)

FAX

CELL/PAGER

NAME

ADDRESS

EMAIL

PHONE (H)

PHONE (W)

FAX

CELL/PAGER

NAME	PHONE (H)
ADDRESS	PHONE (W)
	FAX
EMAIL	CELL/PAGER

NAME	PHONE (H)
ADDRESS	PHONE (W)
	FAX
EMAIL	CELL/PAGER

NAME	PHONE (H)
ADDRESS	PHONE (W)
	FAX
EMAIL	CELL/PAGER

NAME	PHONE (H)
ADDRESS	PHONE (W)
	FAX
EMAIL	CELL/PAGER

NAME	PHONE (H)
ADDRESS	PHONE (W)
	FAX
EMAIL	CELL/PAGER

NAME	PHONE (H)
ADDRESS	PHONE (W)
	FAX
EMAIL	CELL/PAGER

NAME

ADDRESS

EMAIL

PHONE (H)

PHONE (W)

FAX

CELL/PAGER

NAME

ADDRESS

EMAIL

PHONE (H)

PHONE (W)

FAX

CELL/PAGER

NAME

ADDRESS

EMAIL

PHONE (H)

PHONE (W)

FAX

CELL/PAGER

NAME

ADDRESS

EMAIL

PHONE (H)

PHONE (W)

FAX

CELL/PAGER

NAME

ADDRESS

EMAIL

PHONE (H)

PHONE (W)

FAX

CELL/PAGER

NAME

ADDRESS

EMAIL

PHONE (H)

PHONE (W)

FAX

CELL/PAGER

Fuji Seen in the Distance from Senju Pleasure Quarter [Edo]

From the series *Thirty-Six Views of Mt. Fuji,* 1830–1833

Color woodblock print, 25.5 x 37.2 cm (10¹/₁₆ x 14⅝ in.)

Published by Nishimuraya Yohachi

Fuji from Goten-yama, at Shinagawa on the Tōkaidō Highway [Edo]

From the series *Thirty-Six Views of Mt. Fuji*, 1830–1833

Color woodblock print, 25.6 x 37.1 cm (10¹/₁₆ x 14⁵/₈ in.)

Published by Nishimuraya Yohachi

NAME	PHONE (H)
ADDRESS	PHONE (W)
	FAX
EMAIL	CELL/PAGER

NAME	PHONE (H)
ADDRESS	PHONE (W)
	FAX
EMAIL	CELL/PAGER

NAME	PHONE (H)
ADDRESS	PHONE (W)
	FAX
EMAIL	CELL/PAGER

NAME	PHONE (H)
ADDRESS	PHONE (W)
	FAX
EMAIL	CELL/PAGER

NAME	PHONE (H)
ADDRESS	PHONE (W)
	FAX
EMAIL	CELL/PAGER

NAME	PHONE (H)
ADDRESS	PHONE (W)
	FAX
EMAIL	CELL/PAGER

NAME

ADDRESS

EMAIL

PHONE (H)

PHONE (W)

FAX

CELL/PAGER

NAME

ADDRESS

EMAIL

PHONE (H)

PHONE (W)

FAX

CELL/PAGER

NAME

ADDRESS

EMAIL

PHONE (H)

PHONE (W)

FAX

CELL/PAGER

NAME

ADDRESS

EMAIL

PHONE (H)

PHONE (W)

FAX

CELL/PAGER

NAME

ADDRESS

EMAIL

PHONE (H)

PHONE (W)

FAX

CELL/PAGER

NAME

ADDRESS

EMAIL

PHONE (H)

PHONE (W)

FAX

CELL/PAGER

NAME

ADDRESS

EMAIL

PHONE (H)

PHONE (W)

FAX

CELL/PAGER

NAME

ADDRESS

EMAIL

PHONE (H)

PHONE (W)

FAX

CELL/PAGER

NAME

ADDRESS

EMAIL

PHONE (H)

PHONE (W)

FAX

CELL/PAGER

NAME

ADDRESS

EMAIL

PHONE (H)

PHONE (W)

FAX

CELL/PAGER

NAME

ADDRESS

EMAIL

PHONE (H)

PHONE (W)

FAX

CELL/PAGER

NAME

ADDRESS

EMAIL

PHONE (H)

PHONE (W)

FAX

CELL/PAGER

NAME	PHONE (H)
ADDRESS	PHONE (W)
	FAX
EMAIL	CELL/PAGER

NAME	PHONE (H)
ADDRESS	PHONE (W)
	FAX
EMAIL	CELL/PAGER

NAME	PHONE (H)
ADDRESS	PHONE (W)
	FAX
EMAIL	CELL/PAGER

NAME	PHONE (H)
ADDRESS	PHONE (W)
	FAX
EMAIL	CELL/PAGER

NAME	PHONE (H)
ADDRESS	PHONE (W)
	FAX
EMAIL	CELL/PAGER

NAME	PHONE (H)
ADDRESS	PHONE (W)
	FAX
EMAIL	CELL/PAGER

Nakahara in Sagami Province

From the series *Thirty-Six Views of Mt. Fuji*, 1830–1833

Color woodblock print, 25.5 x 37.7 cm (10¹/₁₆ x 14¹³/₁₆ in.)

Published by Nishimuraya Yohachi

Weeping Cherry and Bullfinch

From the series *Small Flowers*, c. 1834

Woodblock, *chuban*, 25.1 x 18.1 cm (9⁷/₈ x 7¹/₈ in.)

Published by Nishimuraya Yohachi

NAME

ADDRESS

EMAIL

PHONE (H)

PHONE (W)

FAX

CELL/PAGER

NAME

ADDRESS

EMAIL

PHONE (H)

PHONE (W)

FAX

CELL/PAGER

NAME

ADDRESS

EMAIL

PHONE (H)

PHONE (W)

FAX

CELL/PAGER

NAME

ADDRESS

EMAIL

PHONE (H)

PHONE (W)

FAX

CELL/PAGER

NAME

ADDRESS

EMAIL

PHONE (H)

PHONE (W)

FAX

CELL/PAGER

NAME

ADDRESS

EMAIL

PHONE (H)

PHONE (W)

FAX

CELL/PAGER

NAME	PHONE (H)
ADDRESS	PHONE (W)
	FAX
EMAIL	CELL/PAGER

NAME	PHONE (H)
ADDRESS	PHONE (W)
	FAX
EMAIL	CELL/PAGER

NAME	PHONE (H)
ADDRESS	PHONE (W)
	FAX
EMAIL	CELL/PAGER

NAME	PHONE (H)
ADDRESS	PHONE (W)
	FAX
EMAIL	CELL/PAGER

NAME	PHONE (H)
ADDRESS	PHONE (W)
	FAX
EMAIL	CELL/PAGER

NAME	PHONE (H)
ADDRESS	PHONE (W)
	FAX
EMAIL	CELL/PAGER

NAME

ADDRESS

EMAIL

PHONE (H)

PHONE (W)

FAX

CELL/PAGER

NAME

ADDRESS

EMAIL

PHONE (H)

PHONE (W)

FAX

CELL/PAGER

NAME

ADDRESS

EMAIL

PHONE (H)

PHONE (W)

FAX

CELL/PAGER

NAME

ADDRESS

EMAIL

PHONE (H)

PHONE (W)

FAX

CELL/PAGER

NAME

ADDRESS

EMAIL

PHONE (H)

PHONE (W)

FAX

CELL/PAGER

NAME

ADDRESS

EMAIL

PHONE (H)

PHONE (W)

FAX

CELL/PAGER

NAME

ADDRESS

EMAIL

PHONE (H)

PHONE (W)

FAX

CELL/PAGER

NAME

ADDRESS

EMAIL

PHONE (H)

PHONE (W)

FAX

CELL/PAGER

NAME

ADDRESS

EMAIL

PHONE (H)

PHONE (W)

FAX

CELL/PAGER

NAME

ADDRESS

EMAIL

PHONE (H)

PHONE (W)

FAX

CELL/PAGER

NAME

ADDRESS

EMAIL

PHONE (H)

PHONE (W)

FAX

CELL/PAGER

NAME

ADDRESS

EMAIL

PHONE (H)

PHONE (W)

FAX

CELL/PAGER

Dawn at Isawa in Kai Province

From the series *Thirty-Six Views of Mt. Fuji*, 1830–1833
Color woodblock print, 25 x 37 cm (9^{13}/$_{16}$ x 14^{9}/$_{16}$ in.)
Published by Nishimuraya Yohachi

Rice Paddies at Ōno in Suruga Province

From the series *Thirty-Six Views of Mt. Fuji*, 1830–1833
Color woodblock print, 25 x 36.7 cm (9¹³/₁₆ x 14⁷/₁₆ in.)
Published by Nishimuraya Yohachi

NAME

ADDRESS

EMAIL

PHONE (H)

PHONE (W)

FAX

CELL/PAGER

NAME

ADDRESS

EMAIL

PHONE (H)

PHONE (W)

FAX

CELL/PAGER

NAME

ADDRESS

EMAIL

PHONE (H)

PHONE (W)

FAX

CELL/PAGER

NAME

ADDRESS

EMAIL

PHONE (H)

PHONE (W)

FAX

CELL/PAGER

NAME

ADDRESS

EMAIL

PHONE (H)

PHONE (W)

FAX

CELL/PAGER

NAME

ADDRESS

EMAIL

PHONE (H)

PHONE (W)

FAX

CELL/PAGER

NAME	PHONE (H)
ADDRESS	PHONE (W)
	FAX
EMAIL	CELL/PAGER

NAME	PHONE (H)
ADDRESS	PHONE (W)
	FAX
EMAIL	CELL/PAGER

NAME	PHONE (H)
ADDRESS	PHONE (W)
	FAX
EMAIL	CELL/PAGER

NAME	PHONE (H)
ADDRESS	PHONE (W)
	FAX
EMAIL	CELL/PAGER

NAME	PHONE (H)
ADDRESS	PHONE (W)
	FAX
EMAIL	CELL/PAGER

NAME	PHONE (H)
ADDRESS	PHONE (W)
	FAX
EMAIL	CELL/PAGER

NAME

ADDRESS

EMAIL

PHONE (H)

PHONE (W)

FAX

CELL/PAGER

NAME

ADDRESS

EMAIL

PHONE (H)

PHONE (W)

FAX

CELL/PAGER

NAME

ADDRESS

EMAIL

PHONE (H)

PHONE (W)

FAX

CELL/PAGER

NAME

ADDRESS

EMAIL

PHONE (H)

PHONE (W)

FAX

CELL/PAGER

NAME

ADDRESS

EMAIL

PHONE (H)

PHONE (W)

FAX

CELL/PAGER

NAME

ADDRESS

EMAIL

PHONE (H)

PHONE (W)

FAX

CELL/PAGER

NAME	PHONE (H)
ADDRESS	PHONE (W)
	FAX
EMAIL	CELL/PAGER

NAME	PHONE (H)
ADDRESS	PHONE (W)
	FAX
EMAIL	CELL/PAGER

NAME	PHONE (H)
ADDRESS	PHONE (W)
	FAX
EMAIL	CELL/PAGER

NAME	PHONE (H)
ADDRESS	PHONE (W)
	FAX
EMAIL	CELL/PAGER

NAME	PHONE (H)
ADDRESS	PHONE (W)
	FAX
EMAIL	CELL/PAGER

NAME	PHONE (H)
ADDRESS	PHONE (W)
	FAX
EMAIL	CELL/PAGER

Fuji from Kanaya on the Tōkaidō Highway

From the series *Thirty-Six Views of Mt. Fuji*, 1830–1833

Color woodblock print, 25.5 x 37.5 cm (10^{1}/$_{16}$ x 14^{3}/$_{4}$ in.)

Published by Nishimuraya Yohachi

Lilies

Color woodblock print, 25 x 37 cm (9^{13}/$_{16}$ x 14^{9}/$_{16}$ in.)

NAME		PHONE (H)
ADDRESS		PHONE (W)
		FAX
EMAIL		CELL/PAGER

NAME		PHONE (H)
ADDRESS		PHONE (W)
		FAX
EMAIL		CELL/PAGER

NAME		PHONE (H)
ADDRESS		PHONE (W)
		FAX
EMAIL		CELL/PAGER

NAME		PHONE (H)
ADDRESS		PHONE (W)
		FAX
EMAIL		CELL/PAGER

NAME		PHONE (H)
ADDRESS		PHONE (W)
		FAX
EMAIL		CELL/PAGER

NAME		PHONE (H)
ADDRESS		PHONE (W)
		FAX
EMAIL		CELL/PAGER

NAME	PHONE (H)
ADDRESS	PHONE (W)
	FAX
EMAIL	CELL/PAGER

NAME	PHONE (H)
ADDRESS	PHONE (W)
	FAX
EMAIL	CELL/PAGER

NAME	PHONE (H)
ADDRESS	PHONE (W)
	FAX
EMAIL	CELL/PAGER

NAME	PHONE (H)
ADDRESS	PHONE (W)
	FAX
EMAIL	CELL/PAGER

NAME	PHONE (H)
ADDRESS	PHONE (W)
	FAX
EMAIL	CELL/PAGER

NAME	PHONE (H)
ADDRESS	PHONE (W)
	FAX
EMAIL	CELL/PAGER

NAME

ADDRESS

EMAIL

PHONE (H)

PHONE (W)

FAX

CELL/PAGER

NAME

ADDRESS

EMAIL

PHONE (H)

PHONE (W)

FAX

CELL/PAGER

NAME

ADDRESS

EMAIL

PHONE (H)

PHONE (W)

FAX

CELL/PAGER

NAME

ADDRESS

EMAIL

PHONE (H)

PHONE (W)

FAX

CELL/PAGER

NAME

ADDRESS

EMAIL

PHONE (H)

PHONE (W)

FAX

CELL/PAGER

NAME

ADDRESS

EMAIL

PHONE (H)

PHONE (W)

FAX

CELL/PAGER

NAME	PHONE (H)
ADDRESS	PHONE (W)
	FAX
EMAIL	CELL/PAGER

NAME	PHONE (H)
ADDRESS	PHONE (W)
	FAX
EMAIL	CELL/PAGER

NAME	PHONE (H)
ADDRESS	PHONE (W)
	FAX
EMAIL	CELL/PAGER

NAME	PHONE (H)
ADDRESS	PHONE (W)
	FAX
EMAIL	CELL/PAGER

NAME	PHONE (H)
ADDRESS	PHONE (W)
	FAX
EMAIL	CELL/PAGER

NAME	PHONE (H)
ADDRESS	PHONE (W)
	FAX
EMAIL	CELL/PAGER

Groups of Mountain Climbers

From the series *Thirty-Six Views of Mt. Fuji*, 1830–1833

Color woodblock print, 25.8 x 37.7 cm (10³/₁₆ x 14¹³/₁₆ in.)

Published by Nishimuraya Yohachi

Portrait of the Artist as a Fisherman
Watching the Moon, c. 1835

Color woodblock print, 21.7 x 18.3 cm (8⁹/₁₆ x 7³/₁₆ in.)